OFFICIAL ANNUAL

School's out for the holidays! Join in the excitement and find eight differences between the pictures.

4

Ice is a wanted criminal! Fill in the missing pieces on the poster.

Check out these photos of the police in action. Tick the object that cannot be found in any of the pictures.

Look at the smaller pictures of the stunt show and circle 'Y' if they appear in the scene and 'N' if they don't.

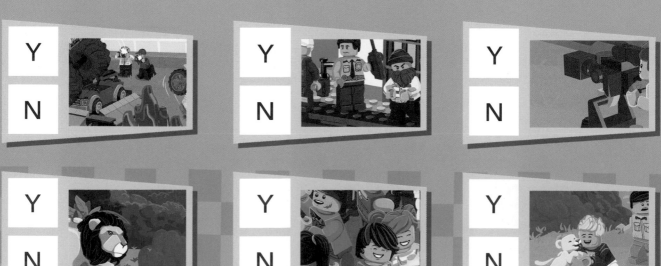

Y
N

Y
N

Y
N

Y
N

Y
N

Y
N

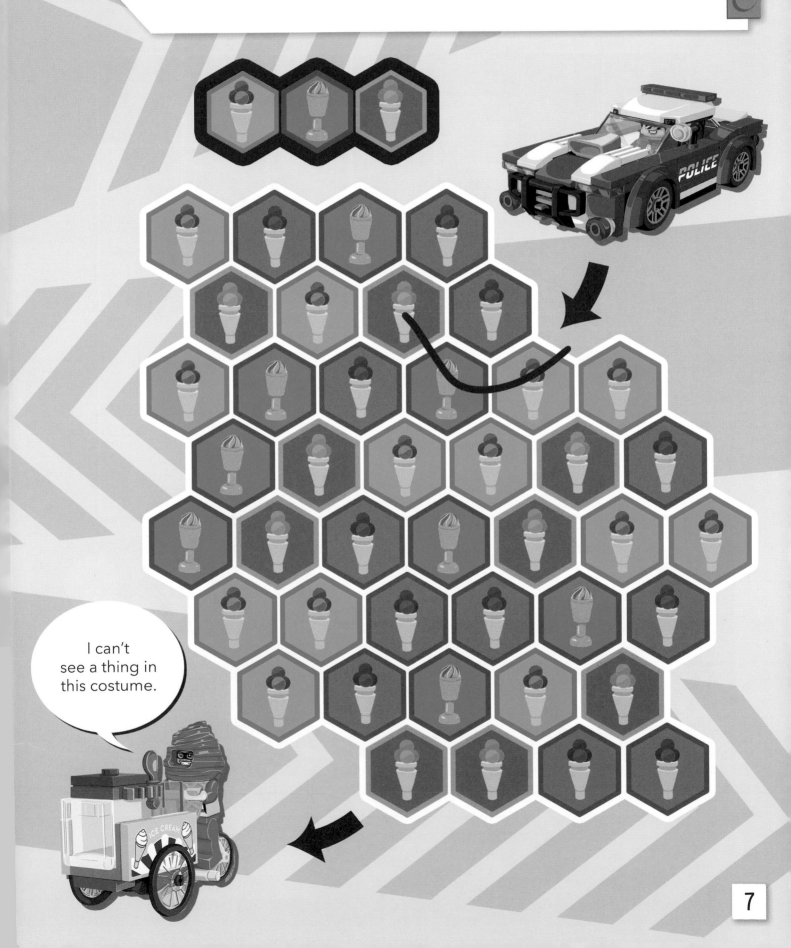

I can't see a thing in this costume.

Time to hit the beach! Spot the items in the picture and tick them off as you go. One has been done for you.

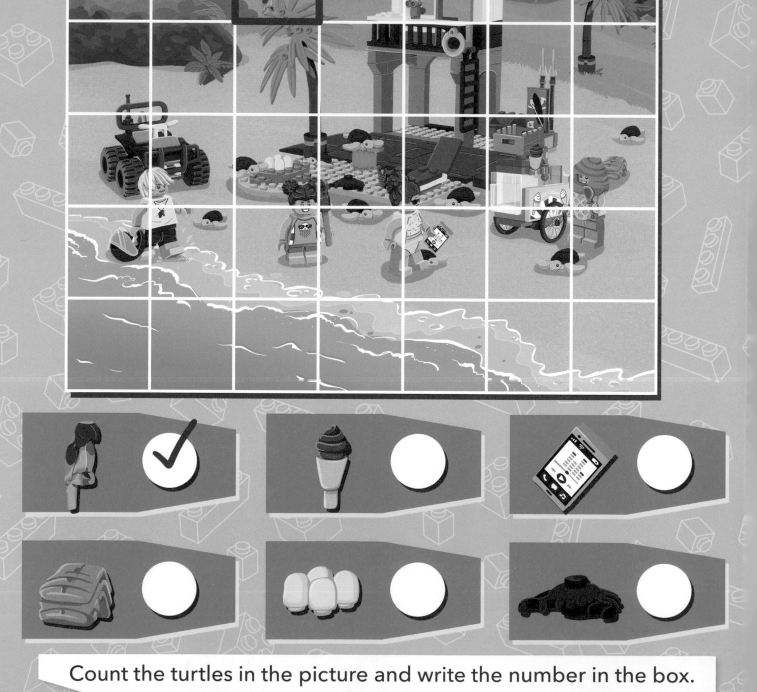

Count the turtles in the picture and write the number in the box.

This ice-cream van is heading for the beach. Tick the parts that you can spot on the vehicle.

Mark the animal in each circle that appears in the next circle. One has been done for you.

START

9

A NEW DESSERT

Ice and Cream, the Ice Cream Bandits, arrived at the park in their van and quickly drew a crowd.

"Ice cream! Get your ice cream!" called Ice. "Try our new special ... salted caramel and papaya!"

Meanwhile, Cream was carrying out the crooks' sneaky plan to steal birthday gifts for their boss. Disguised as ice cream sellers, they were using the van as a distraction while they stole their customers' things.

Cream got started by putting Mayor Solomon Fleck's briefcase and Shirley Keeper's broom and bucket into a sack.

"This briefcase matches the boss's hair," laughed Cream. "The bucket will make a great vase, and the broom can be used to chase away anyone who doesn't bring him back a gift!"

Just as Cream was reaching for Chief Wheeler's skateboard, Wheeler arrived on the scene.

"Stop, thief!" shouted the police chief. "Put the bag on the ground!"

"Quick, let's get out of here!" said Cream, jumping into the ice cream van. Chief Wheeler leapt into his police car and called for backup. "This is Chief Wheeler," he said. "We're in pursuit!"

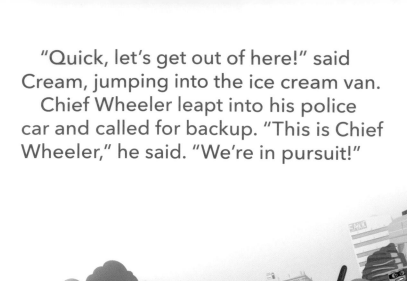

The police helicopter joined the chase.
"Thanks for the support!" Wheeler said to the officers in the air. "We mustn't lose them!"

Suddenly, smoke started billowing out from under the wheels of the ice-cream van.
"Yikes! I can't see anything!" cried Ice. "I think we're skidding!"

The crooks had no idea their smoking
van had sped past a fire engine.
"Stop right where you are," called out
the fire engine's driver, pointing his hose
at the van and spraying it with foam.

The two crooks had no choice but to climb out of their van, and
were coated in foam that looked just like whipped cream. Within
moments they were in handcuffs.

"Congratulations!" Wheeler said to the firefighter. "Not only did
you catch the crooks, but you've also created a new dessert!"

14

Use the dots to colour the picture and discover what the tourist can see through their binoculars.

Untangle the lines and connect the pets to their owners.

These cubs are really cute! Find the small picture that is identical to the big one.

A

B

C

D

This is one fast car! Write the numbers in the correct places so it can hit the racetrack.

2

1

3

4

5

How many times do these animals appear in the jungle scene? Count them and circle the correct total for each one.

8	10
6	3

7	3
5	2

9	3
4	2

What a flight! Circle the shadow that matches the jet.

A

B

C

D

Each of the photos of Madison skateboarding is different. Circle one difference in each photo.

The more fences the jockey jumps over, the more points she will get. Can you work out which route she should take to gain the most points and win the trophy?

Let's go for a picnic in the woods. Can you help the friends get there?

START

FINISH

It's time to hit the road. Write the letters in the correct spaces to complete this camper van.

Everyone wants something different for breakfast. Write their numbers into the circles so each tourist's breakfast is opposite them.

Use the code to colour in the picture
and discover what the space creature
has found washed up on the shore.

Untangle the lines to find out which lucky fan
gets to meet their favourite singing star.

You can never have too many friends to hang out with on holiday. Work out who is missing from each row and write the letters in the empty circles.

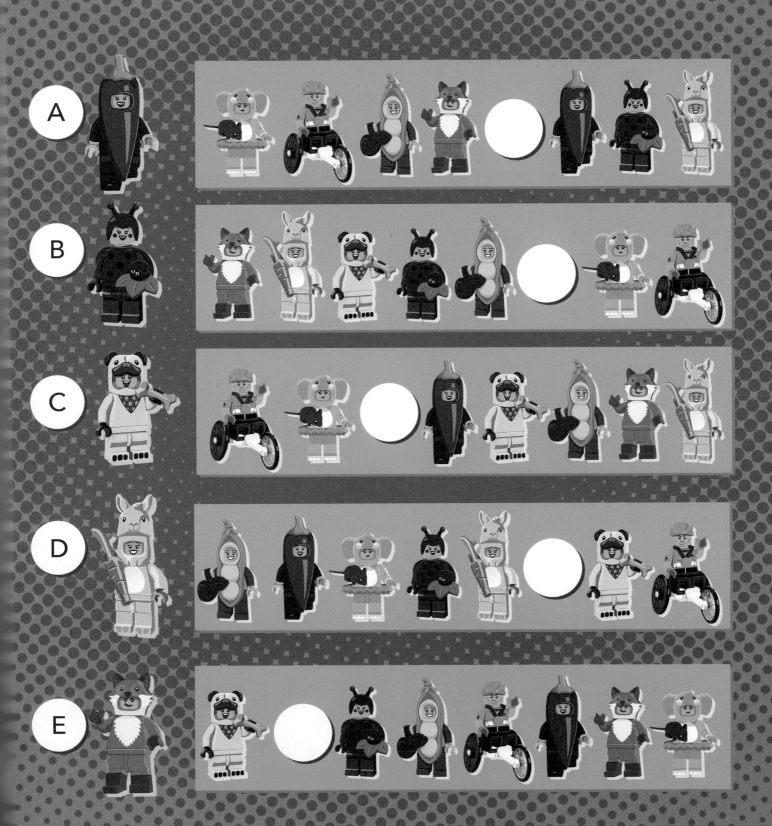

DESERT ISLAND

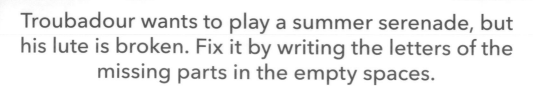

Troubadour wants to play a summer serenade, but his lute is broken. Fix it by writing the letters of the missing parts in the empty spaces.

Maybe I just need to tune it?

The Raccoon Costume Fan's bag hides something that might come in handy at the beach. Connect the dots to discover what it is.

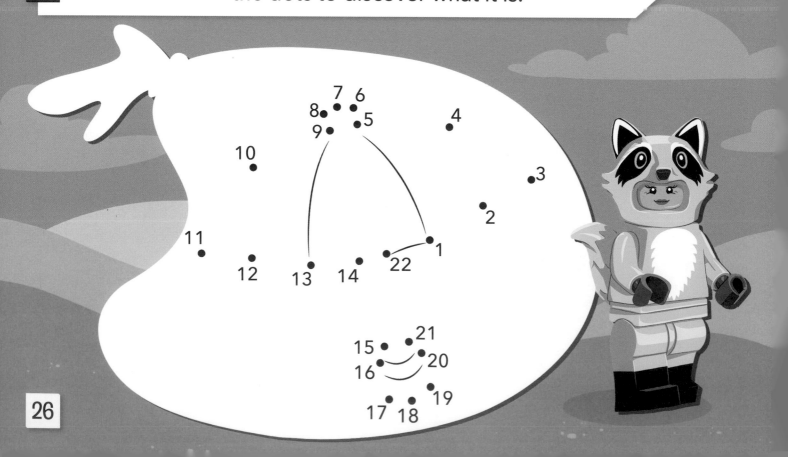

26

Help the castaway get to the ship as quickly as possible. Follow the pattern below to find the way. The first few steps have been done for you.

START

FINISH

Time for an airshow! Take a look at the aerial acrobats and find the one without a matching pair.

Which animal has exactly the same collection of boards in the same order as Paddle Surfer?

The waves are so big!

A

B

C

D

Study this amazing group of friends for one minute and then turn the page for a memory challenge.

POLICE

Circle the six friends you studied on the previous page, without looking back!

Read the clues to work out which of these characters is about to start their fifth frosty treat!

THE ONE YOU ARE LOOKING FOR:

✓ IS WEARING A HAT.

✓ IS HOLDING AN ICE LOLLY.

✓ HAS A MOUSTACHE.

Design your own super-cool robot, with one (or more!) of the functions below. Tick the functions your robot has.

BAKING COOKIES

PAIRING SOCKS

TAKING OUT THE RUBBISH BINS

PET HAIRSTYLING

Put these chilli peppers in order from largest to smallest by writing the numbers 1–7 in the circles. The first one has been done for you.

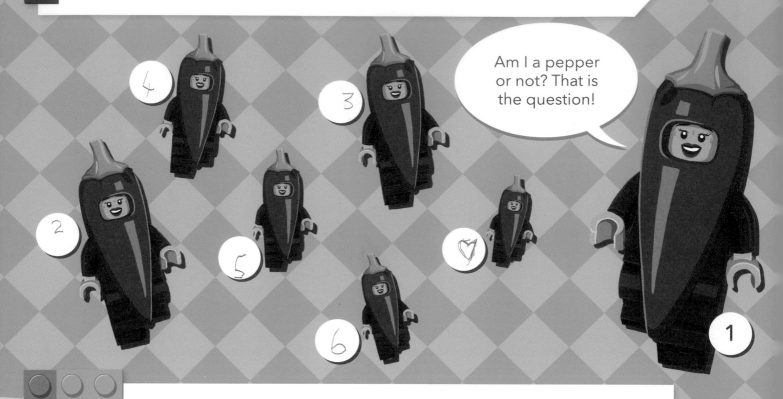

Am I a pepper or not? That is the question!

Work out which character should appear in the empty circle, to discover who won the sandcastle competition.

When is the ice-castle competition?

Show the elf the way through the forest.
Collect as many acorns as possible and
avoid paths with spiders on the way.

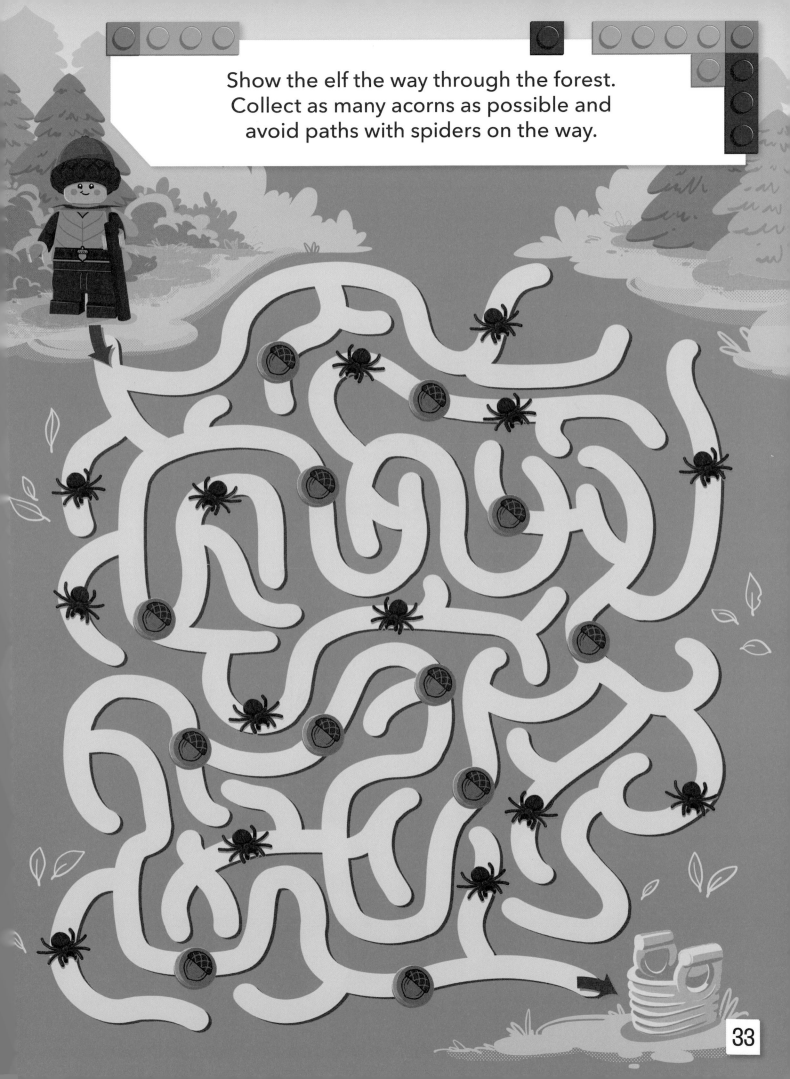

Help this birdwatcher count how many birds of each species she can see. One species has been counted for you.

🦜 **2**	🦜 **1**	🐦 **3**
🦩 **2**	🦉 **1**	🕊 **2**

Quick! Draw a path to lead the racer to the finish line without touching the sides of the track.

These characters all picked up the wrong hats. Give their hats back to them by writing the correct letters in the empty spaces. One has been done for you.

A   B   C   D   E

C   D   E   B   A

WRONG!!

Help Pug Costume Guy find the most delicious bones. Circle the sets that are the same as the ones at the bottom.

Woof, woof! So tasty!

37

Figure Skating Champion is dreaming about winning all the trophies! Help him collect each one without taking the same path twice.

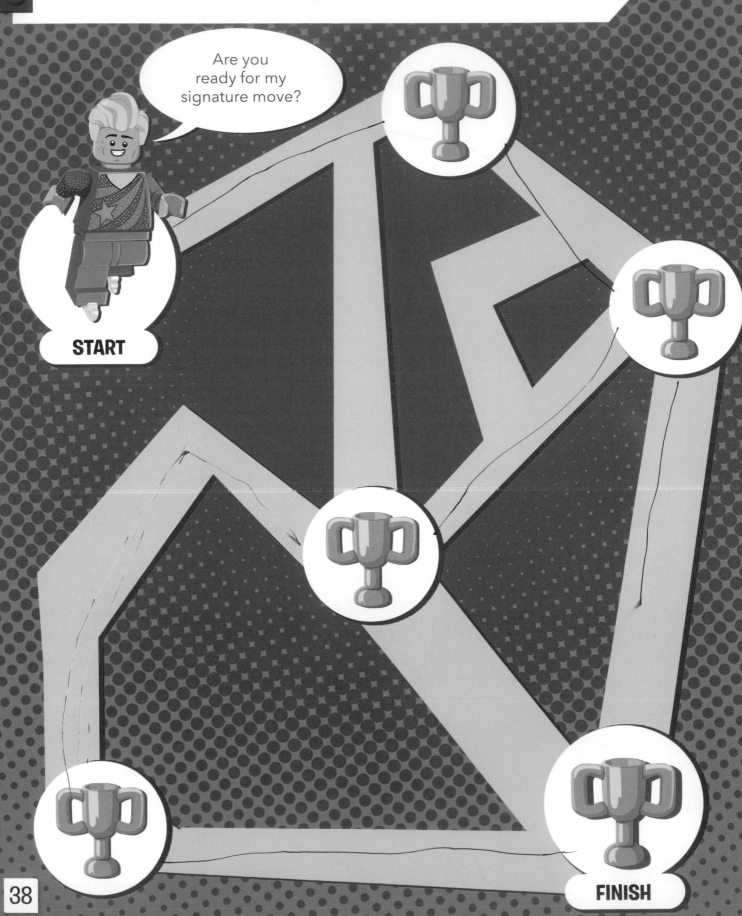

The Centaur Warrior has great accuracy! Write the number of arrows on each target in the empty circles. Which one has the most?

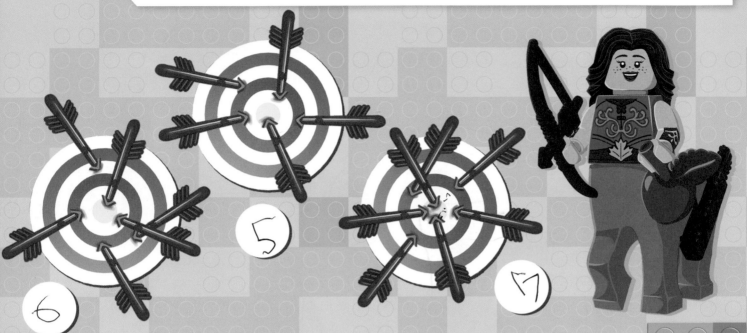

6

5

7

Meet Ladybird! Number her pictures 1 to 4, starting with the one with the fewest details and ending with the one with the most. One has been done for you.

1

Draw lines to connect the torn photo pieces so that the ninja from the world of Ninjago can enjoy some great memories.

Ninja training can be lots of fun! Divide Kai's training shadows into four groups of different poses. One group has been done for you.

Are you ready to move like a ninja?

Villains like to celebrate their birthdays, too! Draw Lord Garmadon's dream birthday present.

Even the Golden Dragon needs a break sometimes. Which of the four small photos matches the faded picture?

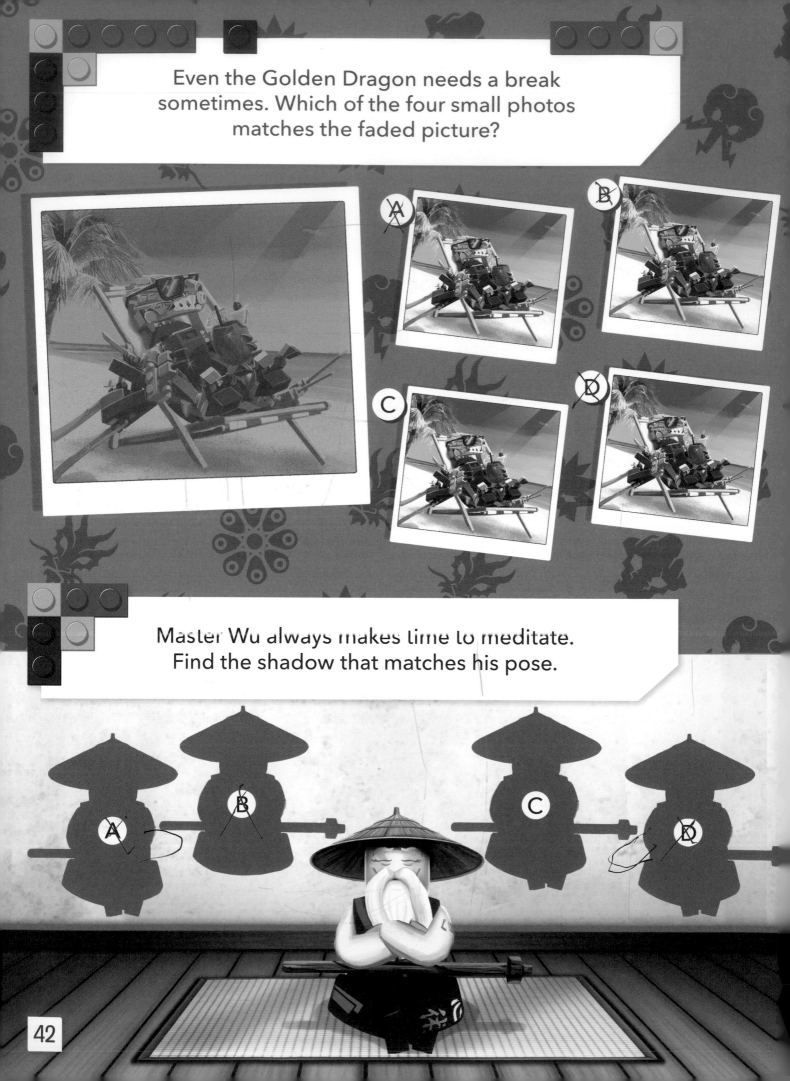

Master Wu always makes time to meditate. Find the shadow that matches his pose.

Packing for a trip can be quite a challenge! Find eight differences between the two pictures.

The ninja like to meet their adoring fans, but sometimes things get a little out of hand. Help Zane escape from his admirers.

Being famous is a really difficult mission.

START

FINISH

44

Nindroids are never on vacation! Complete the Nindroid training sequence by writing the correct numbers in the empty circles.

There's nothing quite like spending an afternoon playing your favourite video game with friends. Colour in the picture to make it even better!

Who is the biggest fan of noodles?
Untangle the noodle strands to find out!

Cole and little Master Wu are singing like
professionals! Fill in the empty stars with the
correct letters to watch their performance.

A

B

C

D

Where do each of these picture pieces appear in the main picture of Kai and Nya meeting the Geckles and Munce tribes?

To be a ninja, you must be observant. Count the shurikens and write the total number in the box.

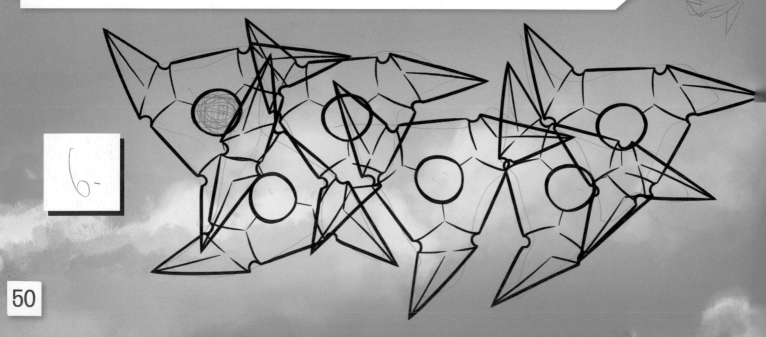

6-

Prepare for an evening ride through the streets of Ninjago City. Which of the mirror images of Nya is the correct one?

A

B

C

D

Look at the smaller pictures of the ninja's workout and circle 'Y' if they appear in the scene and 'N' if they don't.

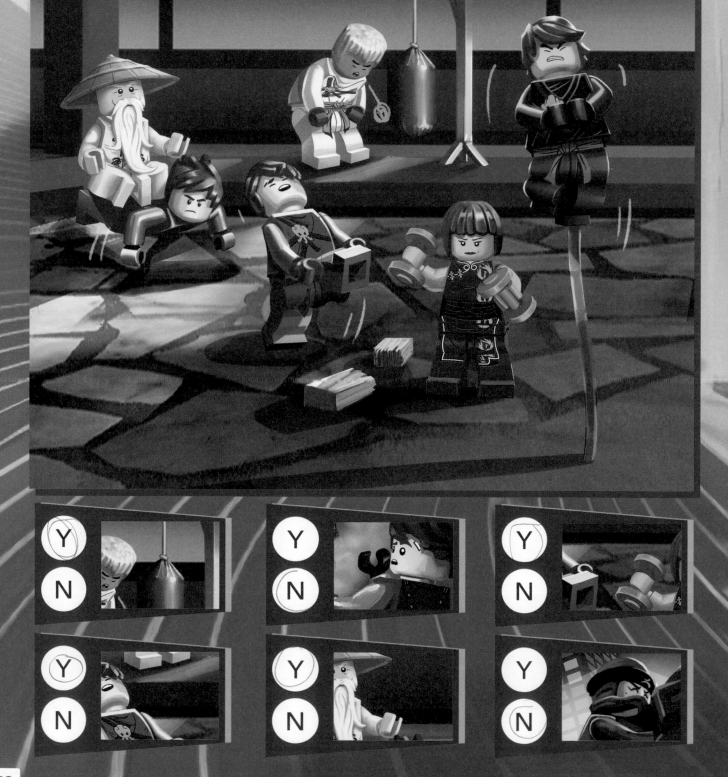

The ninja are almost ready for the beach.
Circle the one ninja in each box who is missing
from the group above or below it.

Garmadon hates getting up early. Help him
out by finding the picture where his alarm
clock looks like the one in the middle.

Someone has crashed the ninja's dinner! Find the one thing in each of the smaller pictures that is different from the main picture.

A

B

C

D

Lloyd wants to get some rest, but Garmadon has other plans. Label the jumbled picture pieces to put them in the correct order. One has been done for you.

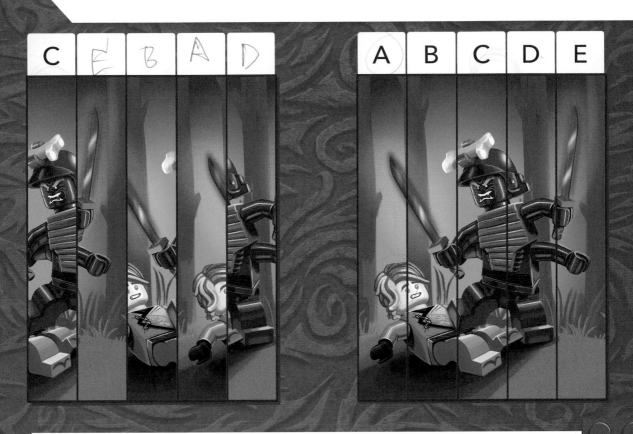

C E B A D | A B C D E

Find and circle the portrait patterns in the grid. The remaining Serpentine is the one that Lloyd was once friends with.

That Serpentine thought my name was Floyd.

Party time! Find all the party items on the left and circle them in the picture.

Kai is helping Master Wu make a snack. Number the pictures to put them in the right order.

It's time for a ninja mission! Complete the jigsaw by writing the letters of the four missing pieces in the correct places.

ANSWERS

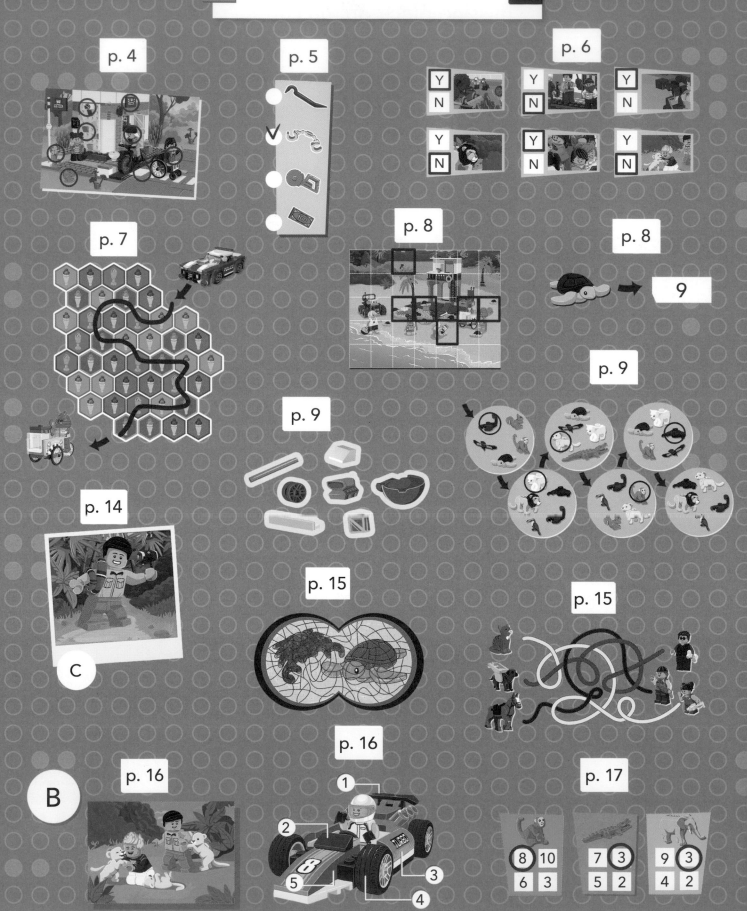

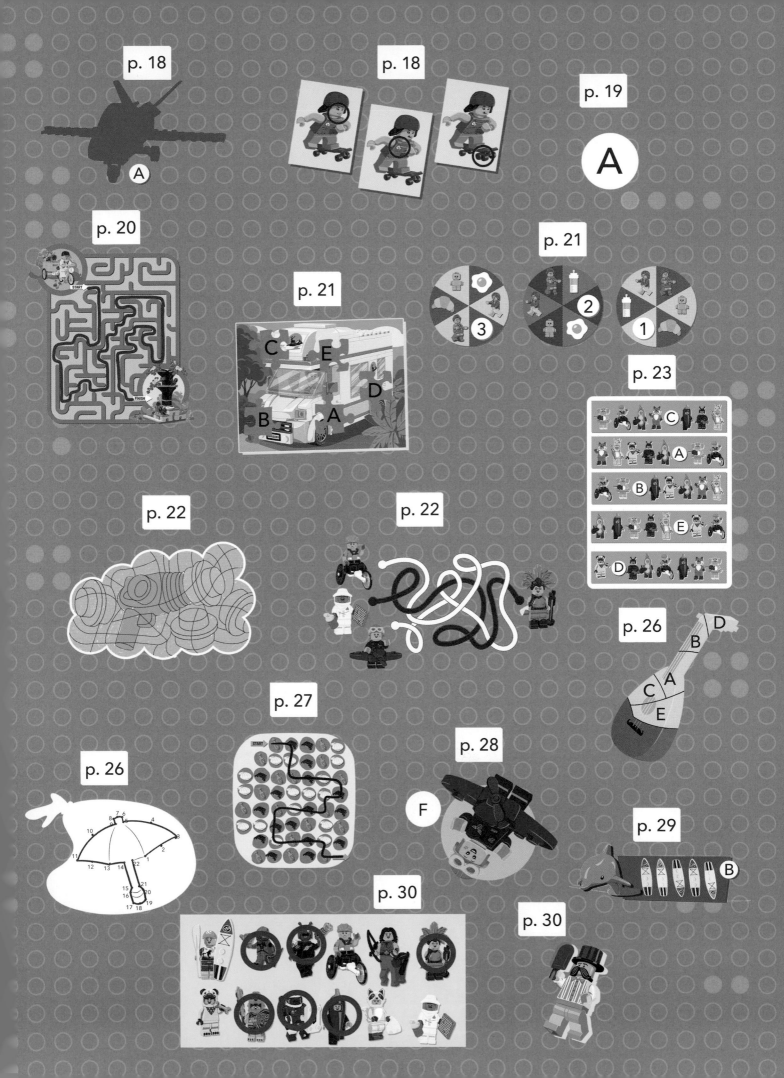

p. 18

p. 18

p. 19

A

p. 20

p. 21

p. 21

p. 23

p. 22

p. 22

p. 26

p. 27

p. 28

p. 26

p. 29

p. 30

p. 30

F

B

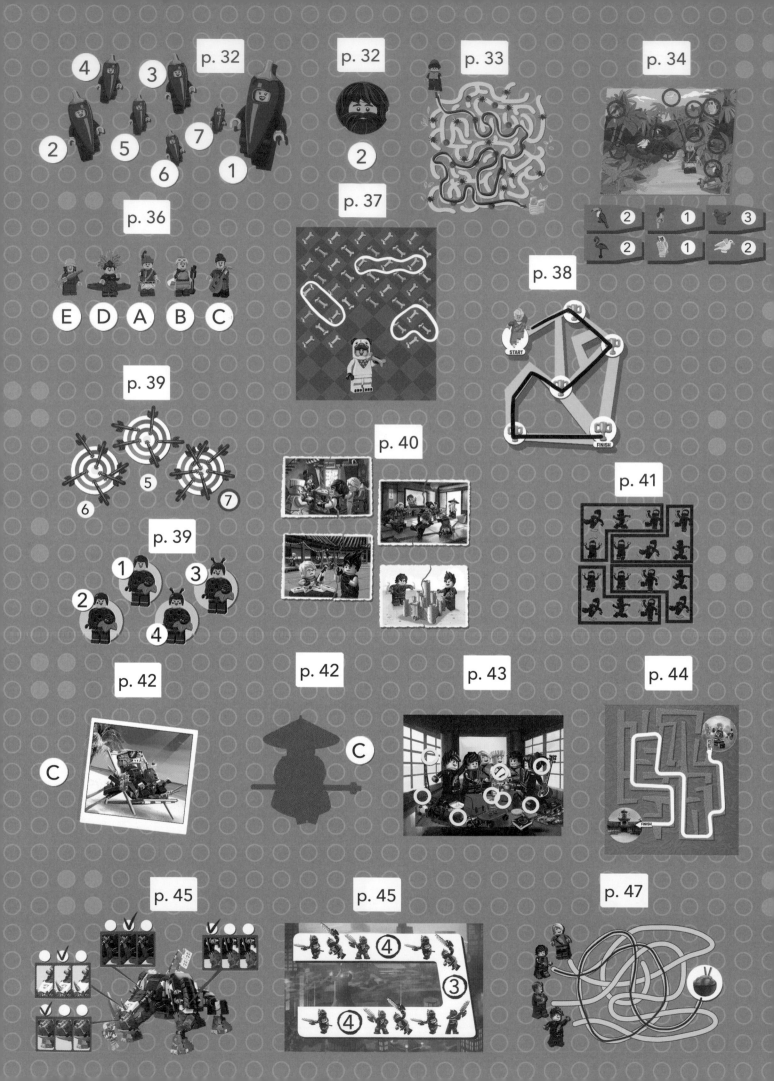

p. 32

p. 32

p. 33

p. 34

p. 36

p. 37

p. 38

p. 39

p. 39

p. 40

p. 41

p. 42

p. 42

p. 43

p. 44

p. 45

p. 45

p. 47

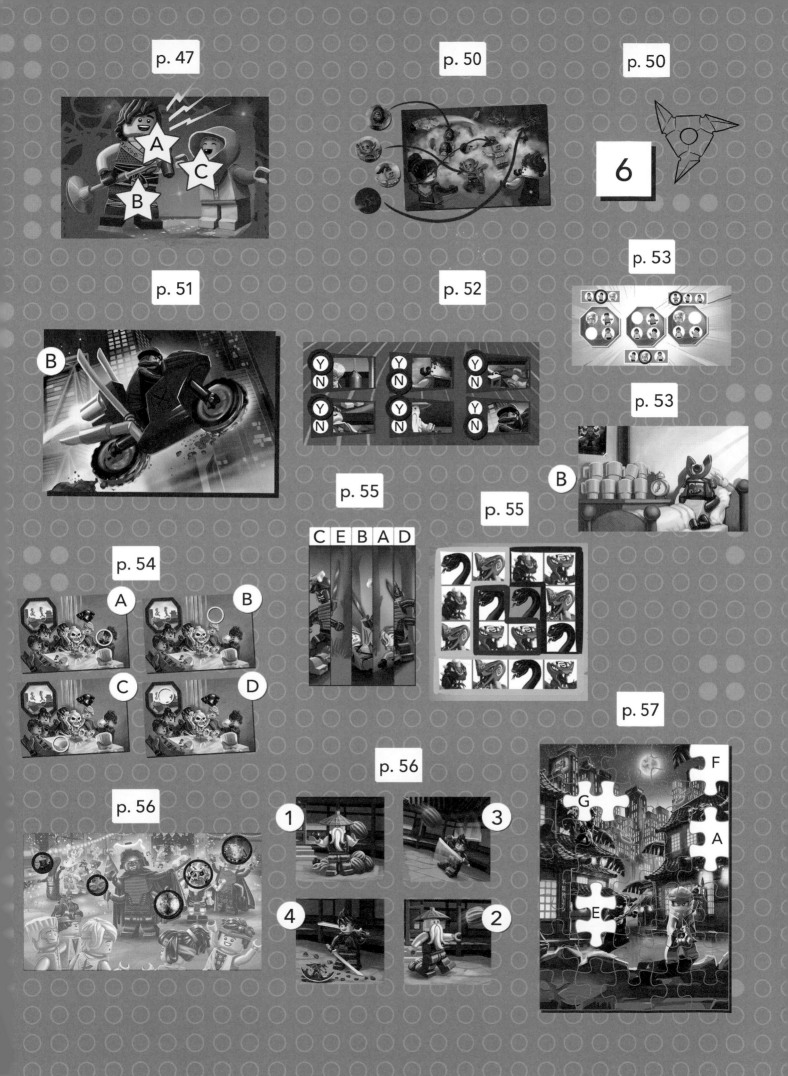

p. 47

p. 50

p. 50

p. 53

p. 51

p. 52

p. 53

p. 55

p. 55

p. 54

p. 56

p. 56

p. 57

INSTRUCTIONS